All about me

My name is _____

I am _____ years old.

I am in Class _____ .

Pictures of things I like best

My favourite food

My favourite toys

My favourite games

Begin with letter b

Draw a ring round each thing that begins with the letter **b**.
One is done for you.

Schofield & Sims

SPRINGBOARD
INTRODUCTORY BOOK

creative writing

word building

comprehension

vocabulary

grammar

spelling

Name

Springboard
Introductory Book

by Chris Burgess

One of a series of English Workbooks

Springboard Introductory Book	0 7217 0883 8
Springboard Book 1	0 7217 0884 6
Springboard Book 2	0 7217 0885 4
Springboard Book 3	0 7217 0886 2
Springboard Book 4	0 7217 0887 0
Springboard Book 5	0 7217 0888 9
Springboard Book 6	0 7217 0889 7
Springboard Book 7	0 7217 0890 0
Springboard Book 8	0 7217 0891 9

0 7217 0883 8

First printed 1996
Reprinted 1997, 1998, 1999, 2000, 2002, 2005, 2006

Printed by Wyndeham Gait Ltd, Grimsby.
Cover design & illustration by Curve Creative, Bradford.

Letters of the alphabet

Trace over the letters of the alphabet.

a b c d e f g h i

j k l m n o p q r

s t u v w x y z

Write the letters in their order in the alphabet.
The first line is done for you.

l e a u k x ➡ a e k l u x

c b m h d s ➡ _____

w f y v g n ➡ _____

t o q r i m ➡ _____

r u j p b a ➡ _____

f z x k u v ➡ _____

j c t o l g ➡ _____

n m e i d s ➡ _____

Begin with letter l

Draw a ring round each thing that begins with the letter l.
One is done for you.

Begin with **d** or **t**

Draw a ring round each thing that begins with the letter **t**.

Put a tick next to each thing that begins with the letter **d**.

One of each is done for you.

Words that rhyme

Words that rhyme are words that sound alike.
In each space there are three pictures. Each picture has its name below it.
Two of the names rhyme. One does not rhyme.
Cross out the word that does not rhyme. The first one is done for you.

cat   car

rat

bell   bee

tree

fish

flag   dish

ball   nail

wall

mouse

rose   house

frog   log

peg

foot   goat

boat

tyre

pear   bear

Begin with letter p

Draw a ring round each thing that begins with the letter **p**.
One is done for you.

Finish the alphabet

Some of the letters of the alphabet are missing.
Write in the missing capital letters.

A __ C D __ F __ H I J __ L __

N O __ __ R __ T __ V __ X Y __

Here are the letters of the alphabet written in small letters.
The letters are not in order.

j q t b i y v l s x c g o d

k u r m a e h p z w n f

Here are the letters of the alphabet in capital letters.
They are not in order.
Write each small letter below its capital letter.

W	G	C	Y	J	P	M

B	O	T	K	F	D	L

U	A	I	V	N	E	X

S	Z	R	Q	H

First letter please

Write the first letter to complete the word under each picture.
The first one is done for you.

J ug	__ abbit	__ indow	__ lide
__ ain	__ ook	__ lephant	__ ebra
__ arrot	__ uck	__ pple	__ orse
__ olcano	__ ite	__ amp	__ eeth

Change one letter

Begin with the top word. Change one letter to make the word shown in the next picture.

Then change one letter of that word to make another word. And so on. The first one is done for you.

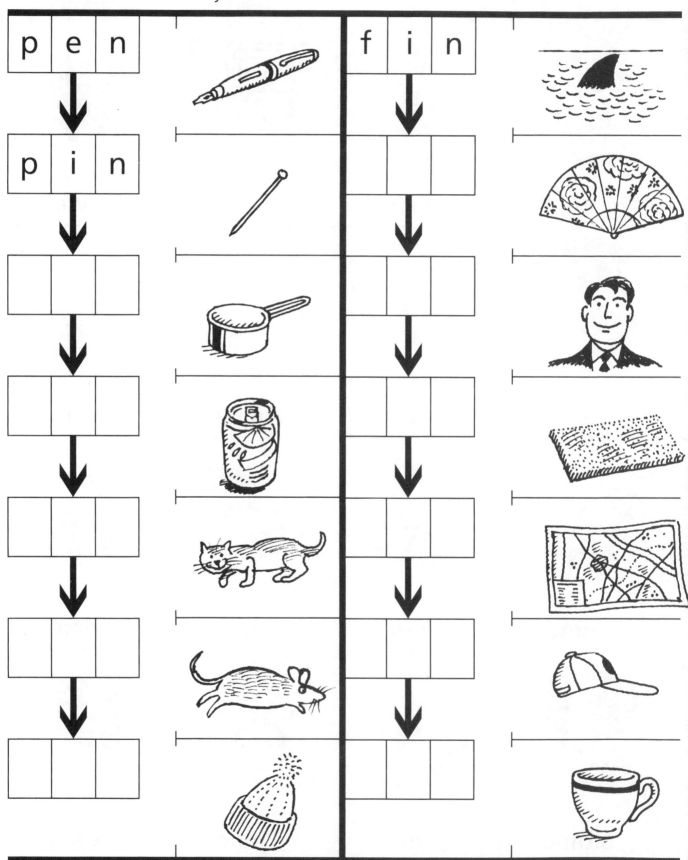

Begin with a vowel

a, **e**, **i**, **o** and **u** are vowels.
Complete each word by writing one of the vowels at the beginning.
The first one is done for you.

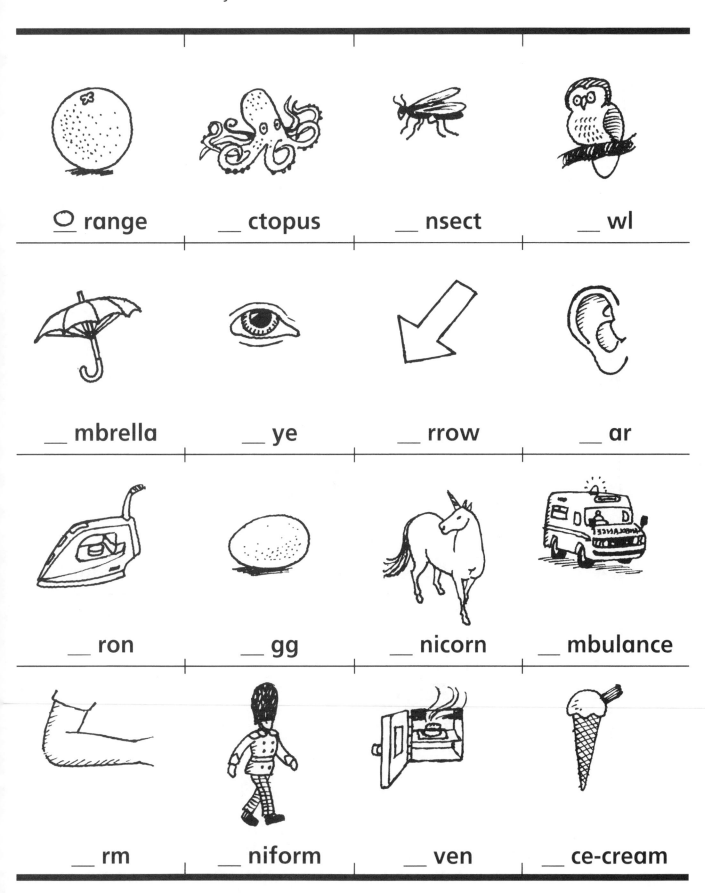

<u>O</u> range

__ ctopus

__ nsect

__ wl

__ mbrella

__ ye

__ rrow

__ ar

__ ron

__ gg

__ nicorn

__ mbulance

__ rm

__ niform

__ ven

__ ce-cream

They go together

One thing in each pair is shown. Draw the other thing above its name.
The first one is done for you.

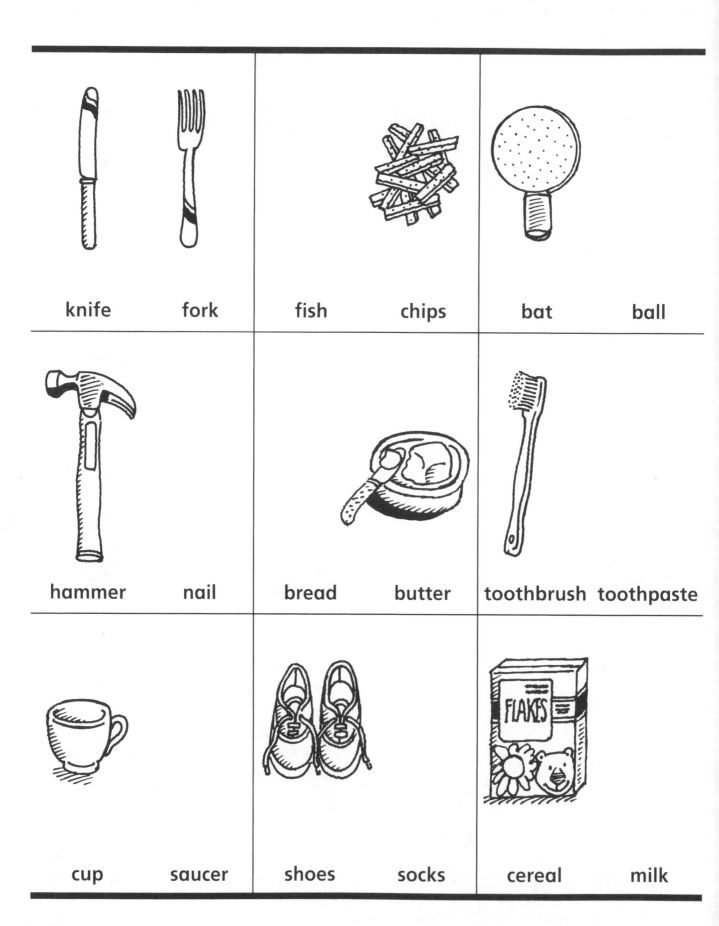

knife	fork	fish	chips	bat	ball
hammer	nail	bread	butter	toothbrush	toothpaste
cup	saucer	shoes	socks	cereal	milk

Begin with letter h

Draw a ring round each thing that begins with the letter **h**.
One is done for you.

The alphabet

Each capital letter of the alphabet has a part missing.
Complete each letter by putting in the missing part.

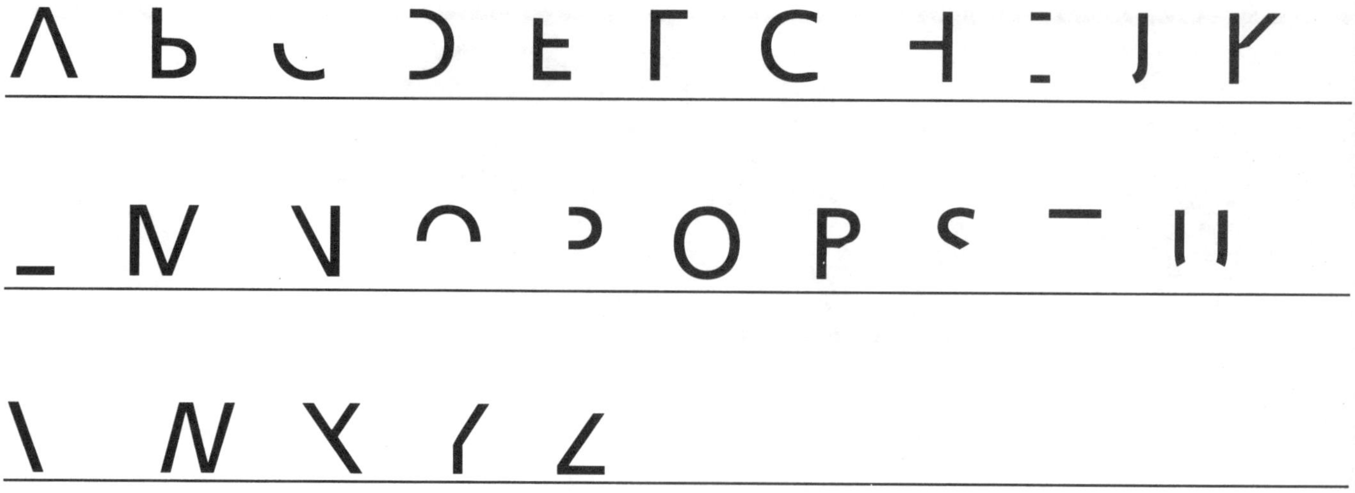

Here are the letters of the alphabet in small letters.
Write the letters in alphabetical order.

p r w l b h t u a j o z d

e q v y i m c x g s n k f

First and last

The words below the pictures need a first letter and a last letter.
Write in the missing letters.
The first one has been done for you.

S tam P

__ ou __

__ uee __

__ abbi __

__ engui __

__ ilkma __

__ adde __

__ elme __

__ uita __

__ oa __

__ i __

__ ro __

__ racke __

__ ompute __

__ upboar __

__ inosau __

Climb the word ladder

The **last** letter of one word becomes the **first** letter of the next word.
All the words you need to climb the ladder are on this page.
The first two words at the bottom of the ladder are done for you.

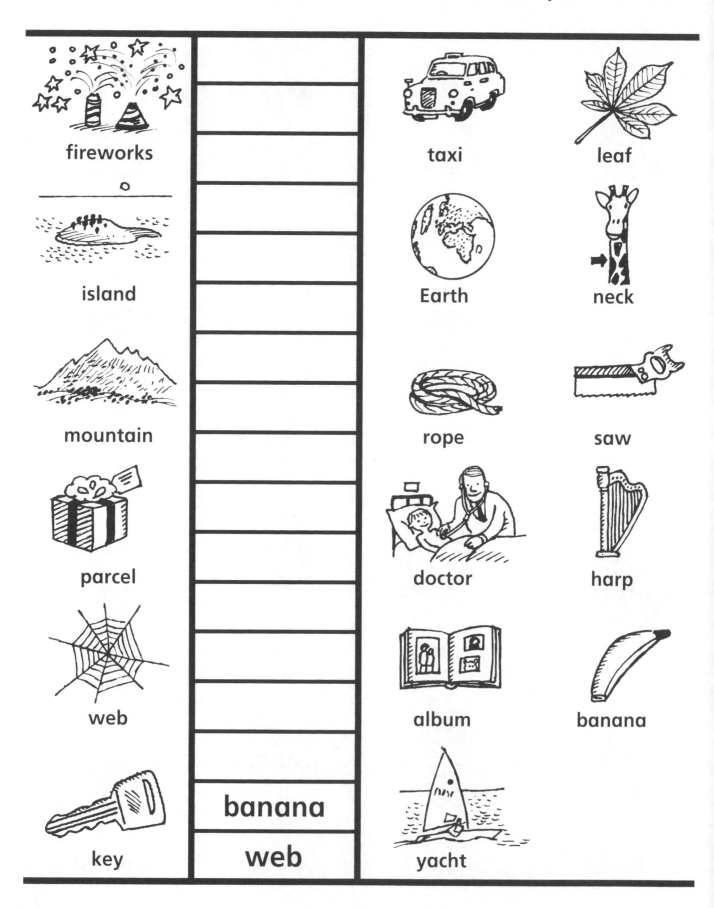

fireworks

island

mountain

parcel

web

key

banana

web

taxi

leaf

Earth

neck

rope

saw

doctor

harp

album

banana

yacht

Begin with g or k

Draw a ring round each thing that begins with the letter **g**.

Put a tick next to each thing that begins with the letter **k**.

One of each is done for you.

Begin with **br** or **pr**

Each word below a picture should begin with **br** or **pr**.

Complete each word by writing **br** or **pr** on the line.

The first one is done for you.

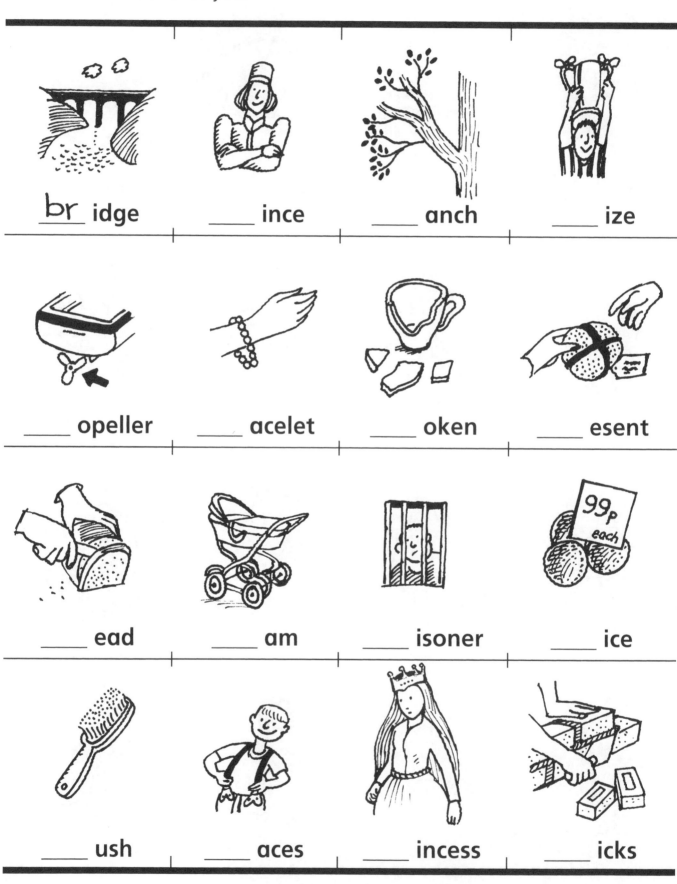

br idge   ____ ince   ____ anch   ____ ize

____ opeller   ____ acelet   ____ oken   ____ esent

____ ead   ____ am   ____ isoner   ____ ice

____ ush   ____ aces   ____ incess   ____ icks

Use the vowel

Here are the five vowels: **a, e, i, o, u**.

Use vowels to complete the words below the pictures.

The first one is done for you.

t e n   c _ r   s _ _ n   b _ _ d

n _ _ t   r _ _ g   f _ _ n   b _ _ x

m _ _ p   j _ _ m   pl _ _ m   cr _ _ sps

t _ g _ r   p _ stm _ n   l _ tt _ r   b _ n _ n _

Begin with m or n

Draw a ring round each thing that begins with the letter **m**.

Put a tick next to each thing that begins with the letter **n**.

More words that rhyme

Words that rhyme are words that sound alike.
Look at each picture and the name below it.
Find the seven pairs of rhyming words.
Write each rhyming pair in the middle of the page. One pair is done for you.

plum

chair

tower

shop

8

eight

socks

bear

rocks

cheese

plate

1 plum and thumb

2 _____ and _____

3 _____ and _____

4 _____ and _____

5 _____ and _____

6 _____ and _____

7 _____ and _____

trees

thumb

shower

stop

Begin with **dr** or **tr**

Each word below a picture begins with **dr** or **tr**.

Complete each word by writing **dr** or **tr** on the line.

The first one is done for you.

_tr_ actor	___ acks	___ ill	___ ee
___ ailer	___ agon	___ ain	___ ain
___ ink	___ awer	___ easure	___ ess
___ iver	___ icycle	___ olley	___ awbridge

A letter at a time

Begin with the top word. Change one letter to make the word shown in the next picture.
Then change one letter of that word to make another word. And so on.
The first change is done for you.

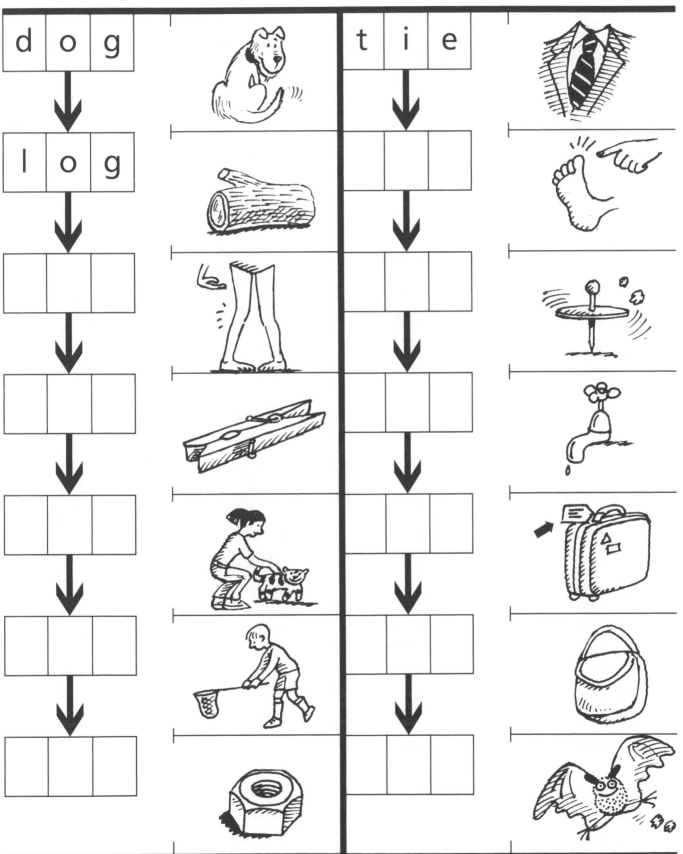

Odd one out

In each space there are three things with their names.
One of each three is different.
On the line write the name of the odd one out. The first one is done for you.

daisy   tulip

tomato   _tomato_

carrot   pear

cabbage   _____

pillow   anorak

T-shirt   _____

tennis racket   table

chair   _____

cake   orange

lemon   _____

bicycle   garden shed

coach   _____

monkey   sheep

sparrow   _____

tree   jug

flower   _____

Begin with f or v

Draw a ring round each thing that begins with the letter **f**.

Put a tick next to each thing that begins with the letter **v**.

a e i o u

More beginnings and endings

The words below the pictures need a first letter and a last letter.
Write in the missing letters.
The first one has been done for you.

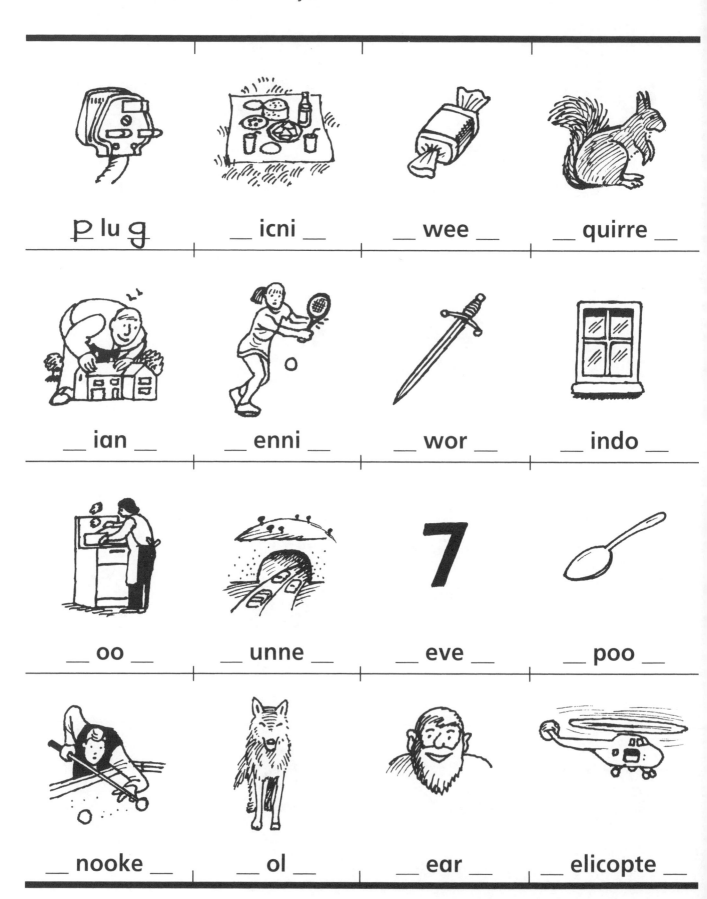

p lu g   __ icni __   __ wee __   __ quirre __

__ ian __   __ enni __   __ wor __   __ indo __

__ oo __   __ unne __   __ eve __   __ poo __

__ nooke __   __ ol __   __ ear __   __ elicopte __

Climb another ladder

The **last** letter of one word becomes the **first** letter of the next word.
All the words you need to climb the ladder are on this page.
The first word is at the bottom of the ladder.

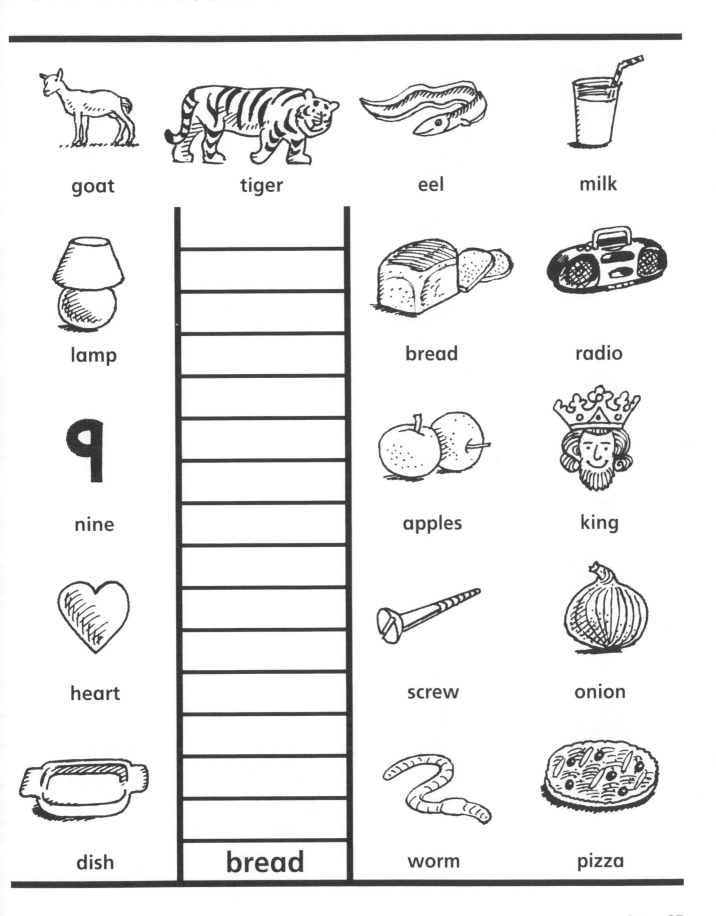

goat

tiger

eel

milk

lamp

bread

radio

nine

apples

king

heart

screw

onion

dish

bread

worm

pizza

Begin with **r** or **w**

Each word should begin with the letter **r** or the letter **w**.

Complete each word by writing **r** or **w** on the line at the beginning of the word.

__ ocket	__ heel	__ hinoceros	__ atch
__ histle	__ adio	__ ainbow	__ hale
__ aterfall	__ all	__ iver	__ ake
__ itch	__ eferee	__ oman	__ oundabout

More vowels

Here are the five vowels: **a, e, i, o, u**.
Use vowels to complete the words below the pictures.
The first one is done for you.

d <u>i</u> g

z __ p

p __ lm

sw __ ng

cr __ wn

j __ gs __ w

c __ m __ l

t __ rg __ t

ch __ rch

sp __ nn __ r

w __ ndm __ ll

a e i o u

v __ w __ ls

w __ rm

b __ ck __ t

c __ m __ r __

__ mbr __ ll __

Schofield & Sims
HELPING CHILDREN TO LEARN

Schofield & Sims was established in 1901 by two headmasters and since then our name has been synonymous with educationally sound texts and teaching materials. Our mission is to publish products which are:

- Educationally sound • Good value • Written by experienced teachers
- Extensively used in schools, nurseries and play groups
- Used by parents to support their children's learning

SPRINGBOARD
INTRODUCTORY BOOK

Nine English workbooks providing a wide range and progressive programme of language exercises. The series covers word construction, comprehension exercises, spelling, creative work and vocabulary.

Springboard Introductory Book - 0 7217 0883 8
Springboard Book 1 - 0 7217 0884 6
Springboard Book 2 - 0 7217 0885 4
Springboard Book 3 - 0 7217 0886 2
Springboard Book 4 - 0 7217 0887 0
Springboard Book 5 - 0 7217 0888 9
Springboard Book 6 - 0 7217 0889 7
Springboard Book 7 - 0 7217 0890 0
Springboard Book 8 - 0 7217 0891 9

Schofield & Sims Key Stage 2 products for 7 to 11 year olds

Language and literacy workbooks

Key Spellings
Books 1 - 4
Pattern and sound based spelling activities and exercises to establish basic spelling skills.

New Spellaway
Books 1 - 4
A progressive series complementing the formal teaching of spelling. New patterns are consolidated, through the 'look, say, cover, write, check approach'.

Posters
Sturdy laminated posters, full colour, write-on/wipe-off, suitable for wall mounting or desk top use. Over 70 titles covering numeracy, literacy, science, nature, geography, history and languages.

Maths and numeracy workbooks

Times Tables
Books 1 and 2
Straight forward tables practice.
Book 2 covers x6, x7, x8, x9, x11, x12 tables
(Book 1 is for Key Stage 1)

Mental Arithmetic
Books 1 - 6 plus Introductory Book
Covers essential mental maths skills through 36 carefully graded tests in each book along with progress tests and diagnostic tests. Supported by a corresponding series of Teacher's Books.

Schofield & Sims

Dogley Mill, Fenay Bridge, Huddersfield, HD8 0NQ
Phone 01484 607080   Fax 01484 606815

e-mail sales@schofieldandsims.co.uk

Information
For further information about products for pre-school, Key Stages 1 and 2, please request our catalogue or visit our website at

www.schofieldandsims.co.uk

ISBN 0-7217-0883-8

9 780721 708836

Price £1.95
Key Stage 2
Age Range 7-11 years